P9-DNY-882

OPEN HIGHWAYS

a diagnostic and developmental reading program

READY TO ROLL

Helen M. Robinson
Marion Monroe
A. Sterl Artley
Charlotte S. Huck
William A. Jenkins
Ira E. Aaron
Linguistic Advisor, Andrew Schiller

Scott, Foresman and Company

CONTENTS

Regional offices of Scott, Foresman and Company are located in Atlanta,
Dallas, Glenview, Palo Alto, and Oakland, N.J.

Goldilocks

and

The Three Bears

window
bed
porridge
chair

The three bears went for a walk.

 Goldilocks saw a little house.

Goldilocks ate it all up.

 Goldilocks broke the chair.

Goldilocks went to sleep.

The three bears came home.

Someone has been eating my porridge.
Someone has been eating my porridge.
Someone has been eating my porridge.
Someone ate it all up.

Someone has been sitting in my chair.
Someone has been sitting in my chair.
Someone has been sitting in my chair.
Someone broke it.

Someone has been sleeping in my bed.
Someone has been sleeping in my bed.
Someone has been sleeping in my bed.
And here she is!

 Goldilocks jumped out the window.

Goldilocks ran all the way home.

How to Make a Puppet

You will need these things.

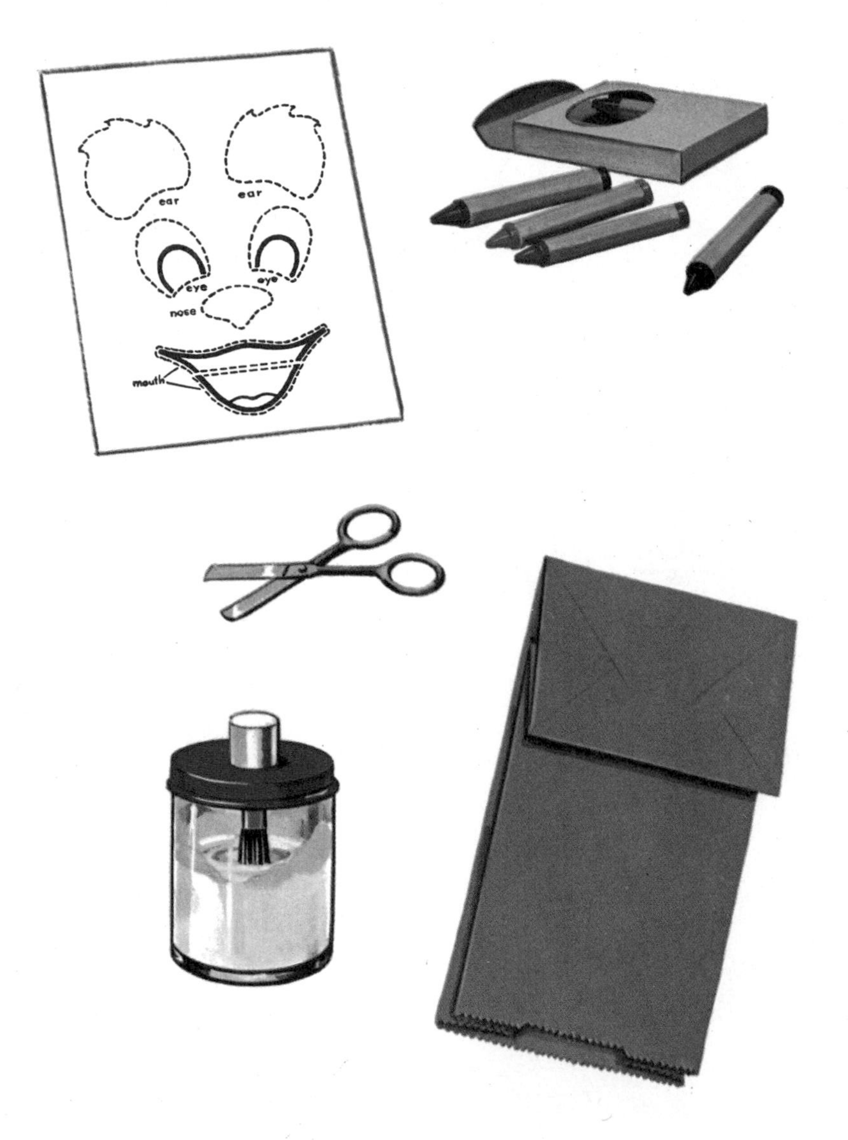

First you will color.

Next you will cut.

Last you will paste.

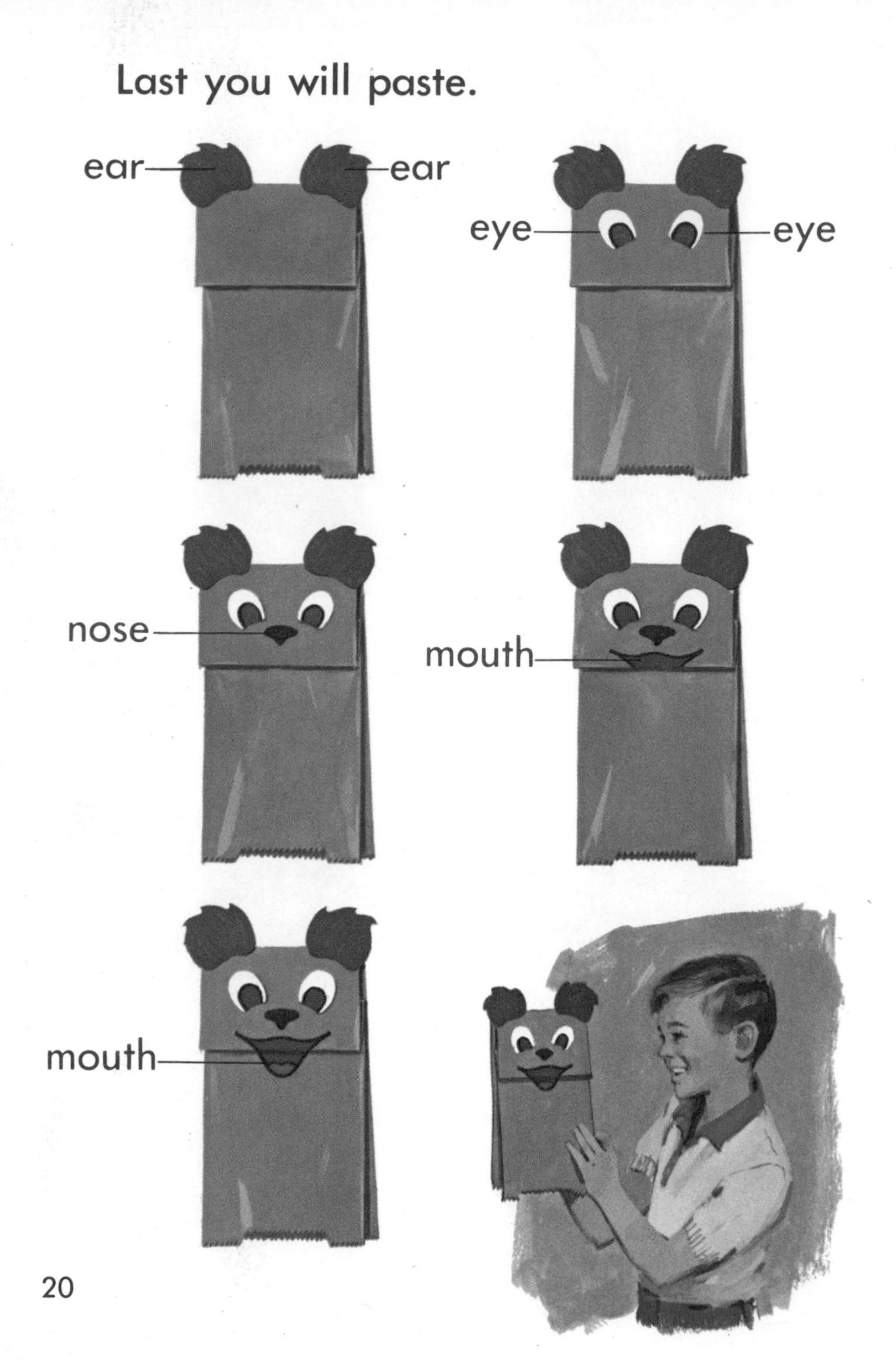

A New Home for Melvin

People in the Story
Mommy
Lucy
Words for Buildings
school
LIBRARY
library

Melvin liked to live with Mommy and Lucy.

Lucy liked to hear **The Three Bears.**

Melvin wanted to hear a new story.

He was going to look for a new home.

Melvin went to find a new home.

The building was a school.

A boy was reading **The Three Bears.**

Melvin went to find a new home.

The building was a library.

A lady was reading a story.

The library was a good home for Melvin.
And Melvin was a happy mouse.

City Child

by Mimi Brodsky

I am a city child.

I live on the tip-top floor

Of an old apartment building

With a very creaky door.

From "City Child" by Mimi Brodsky. *Juniors* (July 1965). Published by American Baptist Board of Education and Publishers.

I zigzag through the traffic.

I ride the playground swings.

I dash down to the subway

As if I had real wings.

We play ball against the steps
And hopscotch on the street
And jacks and tag and giant steps
And even hide-go-seek.

Shadow Tag

Don
Don's shadow
Mark
Mark's shadow
Andy
Andy's shadow

Let's play shadow tag.
I'll be It first.
You run, Mark.

Here I go, Don.
Tag me.

I got you, Mark.
Now you're **It**.

Hi, Mark and Don.
What are you playing?
I want to play, too.

We're playing shadow tag.
Do you see what we're doing?
Now you're **It**, Andy.

My Shadow

by Robert Louis Stevenson

I have a little shadow
 that goes in and out with me,
And what can be the use of him
 is more than I can see.

He is very, very like me
 from the heels up to the head;
And I see him jump before me,
 when I jump into my bed.

Shadows

Ways to Make Shadows

Things to Make with Shadows

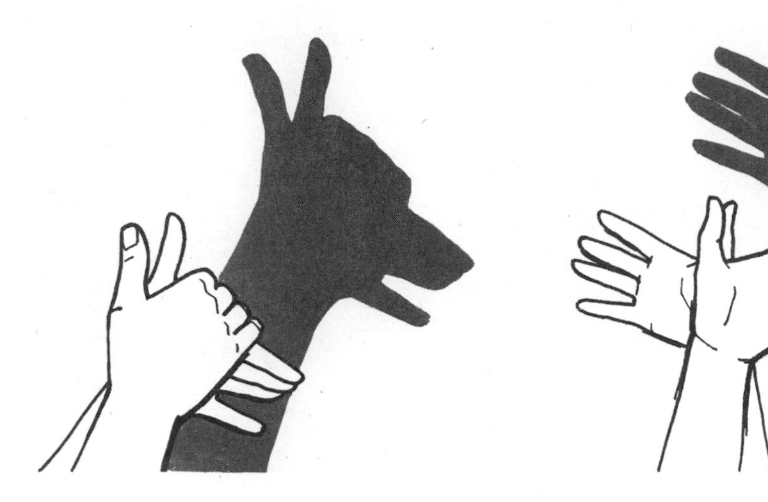

a dog

a bird

a rabbit

a duck

Things to Do with Shadows

shadow plays

shadow walks

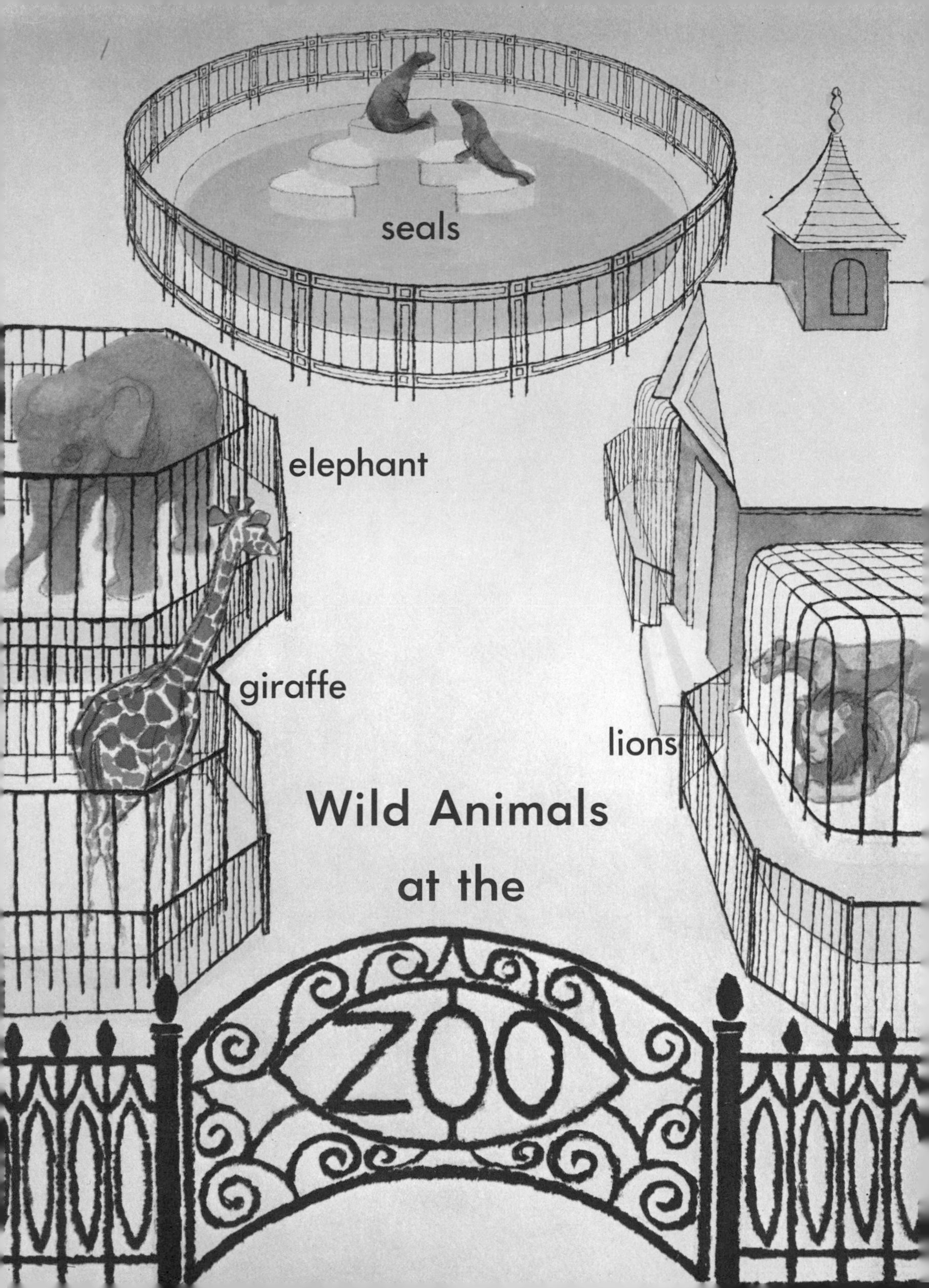
seals
elephant
giraffe
lions
Wild Animals
at the
ZOO

People in the Story

Ted

Patsy

Dad

Sue

Bob

man

men

Dad took the children to the zoo.
First they went to see
the wild animals.

"See the lions," said Patsy.
"There are the father and mother
and two cubs."

Sue said, "Look at the seals.
What's the man feeding them?"

"Fish," said Dad.
"Seals eat fish."

"See that giraffe!" said Ted.

"He took the man's hat."

Dad said, "Look at the elephant.
The men want to put him in the truck.
But he won't go in."

Ted said, "Maybe I can help.
I have a bag of peanuts.
The men can put the peanuts in the truck.
Maybe the elephant will go in to get them."

A man took the peanuts.

He put a line of peanuts into the truck.

The elephant ate the first peanut.

He ate the next peanut,

and the next,

and the next.

The men got into the truck.

"Thank you," said one man. "The peanuts did the trick."

Farm Animals

at the Zoo

Dad took the children to the barn to see the farm animals.

Dad said, "The people
are looking at baby chicks.
Let's look at them, too."

Ted said, "Where are the baby chicks?
I just see eggs."

"I see eggs, too," said Bob.

"Now I see a baby chick!" said Sue.

"I see it, too," said Patsy.
"And I see where it came from."

The family looked at other animals.

Bob said, "I'm a cowboy.
I like that red cow.
I want to ride it."

Ted said, "Cowboys don't ride cows.
Cowboys ride horses.

"Come on, Cowboy Bob," said Dad.
"We'll find a horse for you."

Bob said, "I like this horse.
It's just right for me."

Animal Riddle

What animals can jump higher than a house?

All animals.

Houses can not jump.

The Little Red Hen

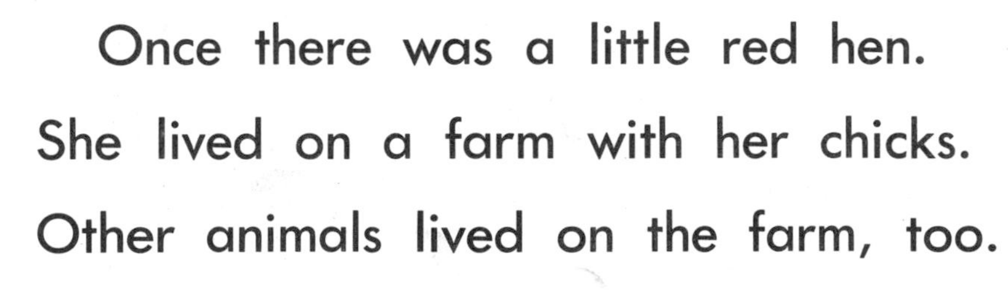

Once there was a little red hen.
She lived on a farm with her chicks.
Other animals lived on the farm, too.

One day the little red hen
found a grain of wheat.

"Who will help me plant this
wheat?" said the little red hen.

"Not I," said the dog.
"Not I," said the pig.
"Not I," said the cat.

"I will then," said the little red hen.
And she did.

At last the wheat was ready to cut.

"Who will help me cut this wheat?" said the little red hen.

"Not I," said the dog.
"Not I," said the pig.
"Not I," said the cat.

"I will then," said the little red hen.
And she did.

Soon the wheat was cut.

"Who will help me take this wheat to the mill?" said the little red hen.

"Not I," said the dog.

"Not I," said the pig.

"Not I," said the cat.

"I will then," said the little red hen.

And she did.

The little red hen came home.

"Who will help me make this flour into bread?" she said.

"Not I," said the dog.

"Not I," said the pig.

"Not I," said the cat.

"I will then," said the little red hen.

And she did.

At last the bread was ready to eat.

"Who will help me eat this bread?" said the little red hen.

"I will!" said the dog.
"I will!" said the pig.
"I will!" said the cat.

The little red hen said,
"Oh no you won't.
You did not help me work.
My chicks and I will eat
the bread."

And they did.

Bill
and
Jill

Words for Things

ball

toy dogs

doll

jacks

logs

tracks

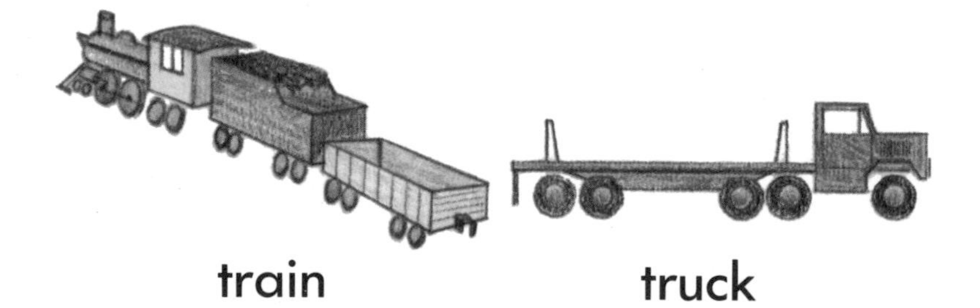

train

truck

Mother came and said one day,
"Children, put your things away.
You can go to the park to play."

"All right," said Bill.

"We will," said Jill.
"We will put the things away."

"The train and the tracks,

The ball and the jacks," said Bill.

"The doll and the dogs,

The truck and the logs," said Jill.

Soon the things were put away.

Then the children ran to play.

They had fun at the park that day.

Where's Wendy?

People in the Story

Wendy and Kim go to school.
Jack is too little to go.
But one day he went with Wendy.
Other brothers and sisters went that day.
Mothers and grandmothers went, too.
They went to see three plays.

Kim said, "Wendy and I are in one play.
I'm going to be Miss Muffet."

Wendy said, "I'm going to be
something funny.
Look for me when you see this."

Jack said, "Where's Wendy?
I want to see Wendy."

"Sh-sh-sh," said Mom.
"This isn't Wendy's play."

Soon Jack said, "This is a new play.
But I don't see Wendy.
When will I see her?"

Mom said, "You'll see her soon."

"This is Wendy's play," said Mom.
"Do you see Wendy?"

"No," said Jack. "But I see Kim.
Kim is Miss Muffet."

Then Jack said, "I see Wendy now.
She is something funny.
Wendy is the tuffet!"

Hey, Diddle, Diddle!

Hey, diddle, diddle!
The cat and the fiddle,
The cow jumped over the moon;
The little dog laughed
To see such sport,
And the dish ran away with the spoon.

How to Make a Cutout

You will need these things.

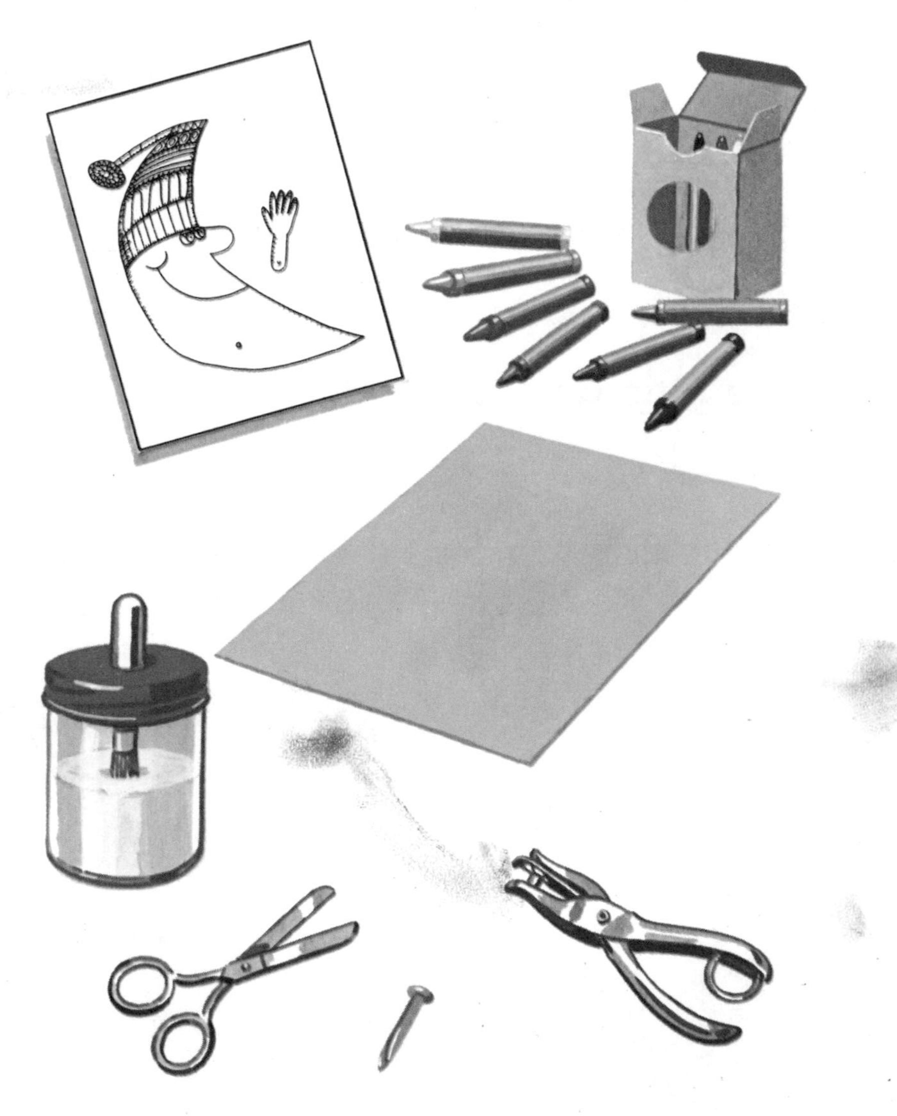

First you will color.

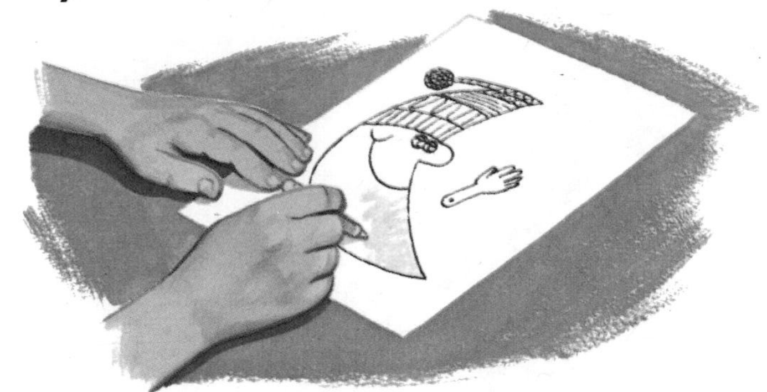

Next you will paste.

Then you will cut.

Next you will make holes.

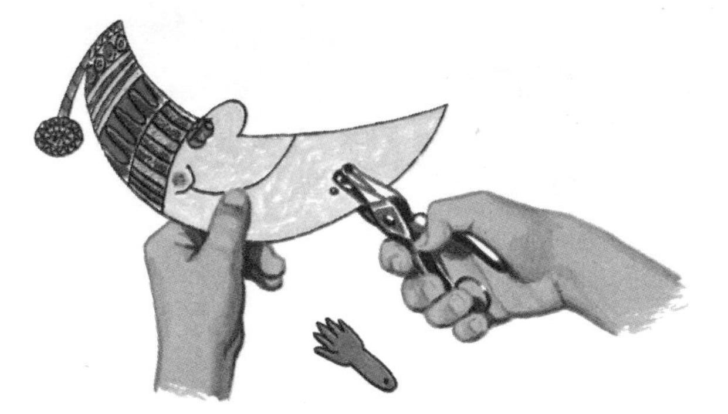

Last you will put your cutout together.

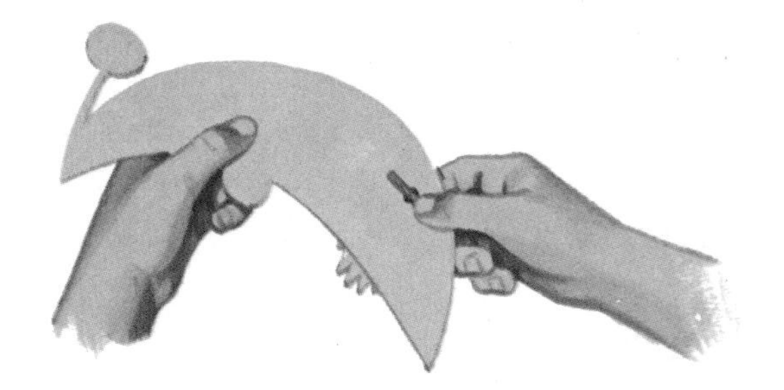

Herman the Helicopter

Herman was a little helicopter who did not know he was a helicopter.

Day after day he said, "What am I? What can I do?"

Then one day Herman saw a boat.

"Maybe I'm a boat," he said.

So he ran and jumped into the water.

Splash! Down went Herman.
"Help!" he shouted. "Get me out."

A big ship came and helped Herman.
The ship said, "You're not a boat.
The water is no place for you.
Go home!"

Herman went home.

He was very sad.

The next day Herman saw a little car.

"Maybe I'm a car," he said.

Herman ran out into the road.

But he ran too fast.

He couldn't stop.

Crash! He ran right into the car.

The little car was very mad.

The car said, "You're not a car.
A road is no place for you.
Go on home!"

So Herman went home.

Herman was very, very sad.
"I'm not a boat," he said.
"I'm not a car. What am I?"

Then a robin said to Herman,
"I know what you are.
Come with me."

Swish! Up went the robin.

Swish! Up went Herman.

"I can fly," said Herman. "I'm a bird!"

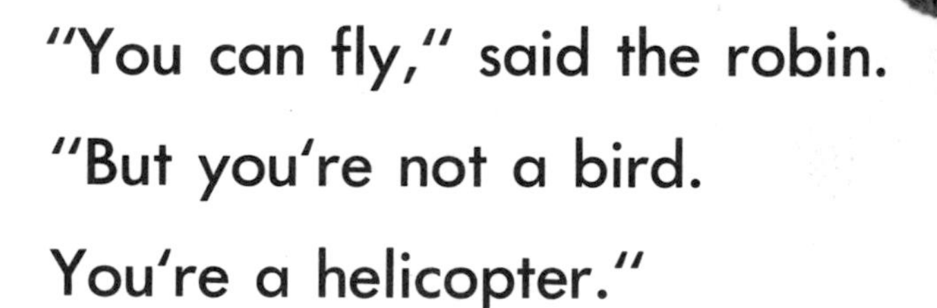

"You can fly," said the robin. "But you're not a bird. You're a helicopter."

"Am I?" said Herman. "Well then, I'm a very happy helicopter."

Acknowledgments

Grateful acknowledgment is hereby given for the right to adapt and use the following copyrighted material:

"A New Home for Melvin" adapted from "The Mouse Who Wanted to Read" by Gina Bell. Reprinted by special permission from *Jack and Jill,* © 1962 The Curtis Publishing Company.

My Shadow from *A Child's Garden of Verses* by Robert Louis Stevenson.

Book cover and title page designed by Bradford/Cout Graphic Design.

The illustrations in this book are by:

George Suyeoka (pp. 5-17), John Mills (pp. 18-20), D. G. Wheeler (pp. 21-27), John Van Dorn (pp. 28-30), Jack White (pp. 31-37, 40-42, 86-88), Bob Keys (pp. 38-39), Eleanor Mills (pp. 43-60), Calvin Merrick (pp. 63-70), Ken Shields (pp. 71-76), Jim Carleton (pp. 77-84), Hy Roth (p. 85), Star Bellei (pp. 89-95).

1 2 3 4 5 6 7 8 9 10 11 12 13 14 15 16 17 18 19 20 A 75 74 73 72 71 70 69 68 67